MW00933554

Dear Reader,

My kids are now older, but when I was in those early,
physically exhausting years of parenting, I was tired—I was opening the microwave
to get the milk kind of tired! I loved when God would give me just the right book
to read to Grace and Caleb that would capture their attention,
teach them about His love for them from a unique angle,
and rejuvenate my own soul in the process!

It is my heart's desire not only to share with your children God's comfort
and love for them but to also rejuvenate your soul in the process, like He did mine.
I pray you and your children will have deep and meaningful conversations
throughout the years as they discover the biblical layers revealed
in the words and pictures throughout this story.

Be sure to read through the foundational Scripture references
listed in the back, as well as record how your child has spied God
and taken steps of faith. —Those will be a blessing to look back on!
May God be honored and glorified as we look to Him to refresh our souls
in our everyday lives! I would love to hear from you.
Please share your thoughts and stories with me at
www.jenashcraft.com.

Please Turn On The Light!

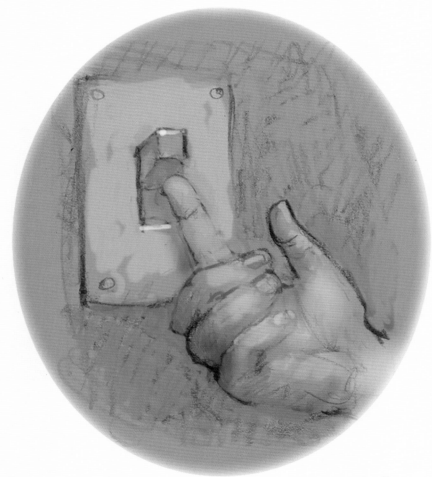

With God's love & care for you!

By Jen Ashcraft

Jen Ashcraft

Is. 40:27-31

TAAE

Please Turn On The Light © 2020 by Jen Ashcraft. All rights reserved.

Printed in the United States of America

Published by Author Academy Elite
PO Box 43, Powell, OH 43065
www.AuthorAcademyElite.com

All rights reserved. This book contains material protected under International and Federal Copyright Laws and Treaties. Any unauthorized reprint or use of this material is prohibited. No part of this book may be reproduced or transmitted in any form or by any means, electronic or mechanical, including photocopying, recording, or by any information storage and retrieval system, without express written permission from the author.

Identifiers:
LCCN: 2020914897
ISBN: 978-1-64746-430-1 (paperback)
ISBN: 978-1-64746-431-8 (hardback)
ISBN: 978-1-64746-432-5 (ebook)

Available in paperback, hardback and e-book

Scripture taken from the NEW AMERICAN STANDARD BIBLE, ©1960, 1962, 1963, 1968, 1971, 1972, 1973, 1975, 1977, by The Lockman Foundation. Used by permission.

Scripture quotations marked TLB are taken from *The Living Bible*, copyright © 1971 by Tyndale House Foundation. Used by permission of Tyndale House Publisher, Inc., Carol Stream, Illinois 60188. All rights reserved.

Scripture quotations marked NLT are taken from the Holy Bible, New Living Translation, copyright © 1996, 2004, 2015 by Tyndale House Foundation. Used by permission from Tyndale House Publishers, Inc., Carol Stream, Illinois 60188. All rights reserved.

Illustrations by Avi Katz. Edited by Allison Myers.

Dedicated

To my 'Deuteronomy 6' mom who excitedly shared
God's love with me in the mundane,

To my faithful dad who pointed me toward God,

To my husband and kids for their
patience and inspiration,

And, above all, to
God for His
renown.

Rachel and Will's mom tucked her kids into bed, turned off their bedroom lights, and left their doors cracked open, but just a little bit. Now it was finally Mom's turn to get herself ready for bed. She felt completely poured out from serving her family all day.

"It's a good feeling," she told herself. "A labor of love." A gentle smile came over her face as she realized this was just what her grandma used to say. Oh, how she missed her and her happy, sparkling blue eyes! But Mom had peace in knowing that her grandma trusted Jesus' *perfect* labor of love and thought, "I will get to see her again in heaven someday!"[1]

With these comforting thoughts hugging her heart, Mom decided to turn off the hallway lamp, which served as a night-light for her two little ones. She made her way down the hall, clicked off the light, and slowly tip-toed away, only to hear...

"Mommy! Mommy! I'm afraid! Please turn on the light!"

Mom quickly asked God for energy and patience as she walked back into Rachel's bedroom.

"Oh, Rachel, there's nothing to be afraid of. I know—how about we play 'I Spy!?' But this time, let's look for where we see God. By playing 'I Spy' for God, He'll help us remember that He's right here with us and then you won't feel so scared anymore!"

Rachel sat up quickly. She loved playing 'I Spy' with her mom!

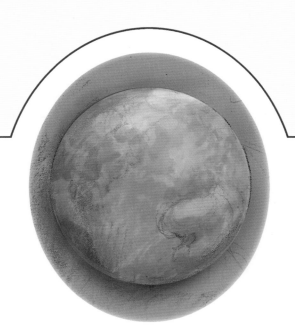

"Okay, here we go!" Mom said, looking forward to what God was going to do.

"I spy, in the beginning of time, when God created the heavens and the earth that He purposely created everything in a certain order. Do you want to guess what God created right after He made the heavens and the earth?"

"I don't remember the order. Was it trees?"

"No."

"Monkeys!?!"

"No."

"Bugs?"

"No, but those are good guesses. God created light![2] And do you want to guess why He created light right away?"

Rachel thought for a moment and jokingly said, "Was it because He needed to see what He was doing?"

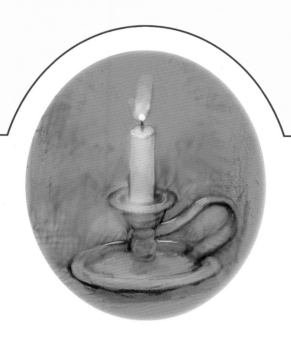

"No, silly!" Mom said with a big smile. "God doesn't need to turn on lights to see. Light actually comes from Him. He's like a big flashlight. God tells us in His love letter, the Bible, that He *is* light and in Him there is no darkness at all."[3]

"That's neat! But Mommy, if God is light and could already see, why did He need to create light?"

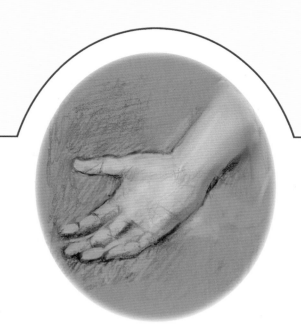

"Well, I think that God created light because He cares about us and doesn't want us to be afraid."

"Huh," Rachel said with a puzzled look on her face. "But people weren't even made yet, right? So how could they be afraid?"

"True, but God knew He was going to make them, so He wanted to get everything ready for them first. Kind of like when we get ready for our Christmas party. We clean the whole house and turn on all the lights to welcome our guests."

Rachel's eyes grew wider as she was trying to imagine all that her mom was telling her.

Mom continued, "And you know how God the Father says that His Son Jesus is the Light of the world?"[4]

"Yes," Rachel eagerly said. "Mrs. Rea just talked about that in my class at church last Sunday."

"Oh good! Well, just like God created light in the sky for us so that we wouldn't be afraid, even better, God sent His light to earth in Jesus so that we wouldn't be afraid.[5] God really doesn't want us to be afraid of the dark. *You see, wherever Jesus is, He chases the darkness away!*[6] Wasn't that so very kind and loving of God to send Jesus to us!?"

"Yes! I like that a lot! I never thought of Jesus like that before. When He comes into a room, it's like the light turns on!"

Rachel was quiet for a moment and asked, "Since Jesus is the Light of the world and since we turn on lights to welcome people into our home, can 'I Spy' then that God sent Jesus as His light to welcome people into His home?"

"Absolutely! I like how you said that, Rachel."

"Thanks, Mommy!"

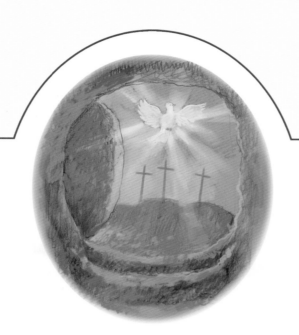

Mom was on the edge of her seat with anticipation. "And do you want to 'spy' one more amazing place where we see God?"

"Yes, please!"

"Remember when you told Dad and me that you needed Jesus? You agreed that He is God's Son and believed in your heart that you were made clean when His Father raised Him from the dead.[7] Well, when you did that, God put His Light *inside you*!"

"What do you mean, Mommy? Do you mean I have a light bulb in me somewhere?"

Mom chuckled. "Close! God's love letter says that at the very moment we trusted Jesus, God gave us His Holy Spirit to live inside us."[8]

Rachel blurted out, "You mean it's like *God put His 'Night-Light' inside me*!?!"

"Yes! And now you don't need to be afraid of the dark anymore! *His 'Night-Light' in you is more powerful than the darkness around you!* How does that make you feel about the dark now?"

"I'm less scared, A LOT less scared, of the dark now! God is amazing!"

"I agree; He is amazing!" Mom said with a huge smile. "And there's one more important thing for us to 'spy' about God's 'Night-Light,' and we can talk more about this tomorrow—*God put His 'Night-Light' in you not only to help you, but for Him to help others through you too.*"

Rachel, dreamy-eyed, whispered under her breath, "You mean, He's going to use me to help other people be brave too!?" Her eyes widened, "Mommy, could we sing that song you taught me?"

"What song is that?"

"That song where we pretend our finger is a candle."

Mom smiled and said, "Do you mean 'This Little Light of Mine?'"

"Yes!" She cheered. "That's it!"

They sang quietly so as not to wake Will. But inside, Rachel was shouting with joy and confidence in God. She was no longer filled with fear but with peace and courage. She had God's Holy Spirit in her and He was her 'Night-Light' Who is more powerful than the darkness around her.

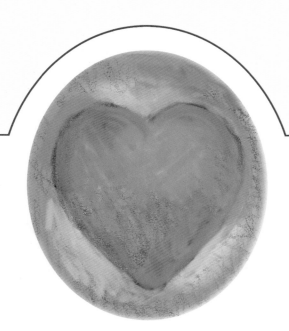

Once they finished singing, they thanked God the Father for sending Jesus. Then they thanked Jesus for being the Light of the world and for His perfect labor of love. And then lastly, they thanked the Holy Spirit for shining the light of Jesus through them to give them courage in the darkness.

By now Rachel's eyelids were very heavy and she said through a yawn, "Mommy, I spy something."

"What's that?"

"I spy that God's 'Night-Light' in me is making me brave. You can turn off the hall light now, if you want."

Mom whispered, "That's wonderful, Rachel!" She kissed her on the forehead and softly said, "I love you with all of my heart!"

Mom made her way back to the hallway lamp, clicked off the light, and thanked God for giving her that sweet time with her treasured daughter.[10]

Rachel rolled over and whispered "I love you with all my heart too, Mommy." She closed her eyes and peacefully fell fast asleep.

"In peace I will lie down and sleep,
for You alone, O LORD,
will keep me safe."

(Psalm 4:8 NLT)

Foundational Scripture...

1. Isaiah 53:11b-12 "...**My Servant, will justify the many,** as He will bear their iniquities. Therefore, I will allot Him a portion with the great, and He will divide the booty with the strong; **because He poured out Himself to death**, and was numbered with the transgressors; yet He Himself bore the sin of many, and interceded for the transgressors." (NASB; emphasis added)

   I John 3:5 "...**He appeared in order to take away sins; and in Him there is no sin.**" (NASB; emphasis added)

2. Genesis 1:1-5 "When God began creating the heavens and the earth, the earth was a shapeless, chaotic mass, with the Spirit of God brooding over the dark vapors. Then **God said, 'Let there be light.'** And light appeared. And God was pleased with it and divided the light from the darkness. He called the light 'daytime,' and the darkness 'nighttime.' Together they formed the first day." (TLB; emphasis added)

3. 1 John 1:5b "...**God is light**, and in Him there is no darkness at all." (NASB; emphasis added)

4. Luke 9:35 **"Then a voice came out of the cloud, saying, 'This is My Son, My Chosen One; listen to Him!'"** (NASB; emphasis added)

   John 8:12 "Then Jesus again spoke to them, saying, '**I am the Light of the world; he who follows Me will not walk in the darkness**, but will have the Light of life." (NASB; emphasis added)

   2 Corinthians 4:6 "For **God**, who said, 'Light shall shine out of darkness,' is the One who **has shone** in our hearts to give **the light of the knowledge of the glory of God in the face of Christ**." (NASB; emphasis added)

5. Psalm 91:5 **"Now you don't need to be afraid of the dark anymore**, nor fear the dangers of the day;" (TLB; emphasis added)

6. John 1:1-5 "Before anything else existed, there was Christ, with God. He has always been alive and is himself God. He created everything there is—nothing exists that he didn't make. **Eternal life is in him, and this life gives light to all mankind. His life is the light that shines through the darkness—and the darkness can never extinguish it.**" (TLB; emphasis added)

7. Romans 10:9-10 "...**if you confess with your mouth Jesus as Lord, and believe in your heart that God raised Him from the dead, you shall be saved**; for with the heart man believes, resulting in righteousness, and with the mouth he confesses, resulting in salvation." (NASB; emphasis added)

Hebrews 10:10 "Under this new plan we have been **forgiven and made clean by Christ's dying for us once and for all.**" (TLB; emphasis added)

Titus 3:4-7 "But when the kindness of God our Savior and *His* love for mankind appeared, **He saved us**, not on the basis of deeds which we have done in righteousness, but **according to His mercy**, by the washing of regeneration and renewing **by the Holy Spirit, whom He poured out upon us richly through Jesus Christ our Savior**, so that being justified by His grace we would be made heirs according to *the* hope of eternal life." (NASB; emphasis added)

John 3:16-17 "**For God loved the world so much that he gave his only Son so that anyone who believes in him shall not perish but have eternal life. God did not send his Son into the world to condemn it, but to save it.**" (TLB; emphasis added)

8. John 14:16-17 "**I will ask the Father, and He will give you another Helper**, that He may be with you forever; *that is* the **Spirit of truth**, whom the world cannot receive, because it does not see Him or know Him, *but* you know Him because **He abides with you and will be in you.**" (NASB; emphasis added)

Ephesians 1:13-14 "In Him, you also, after listening to the message of truth, the gospel of your salvation —having also believed, **you were sealed in Him with the Holy Spirit** of promise, who is given as a pledge of our inheritance,..." (NASB; emphasis added)

9. Matthew 5:14-16 "You are the world's light—a city on a hill, glowing in the night for all to see. **Don't hide your light! Let it shine for all**; let your good deeds glow for all to see, so **that they will praise your heavenly Father.**" (TLB; emphasis added)

Galatians 5:22 "**But when the Holy Spirit controls our lives He will produce this kind of fruit in us**: love, joy, peace, patience, kindness, goodness, faithfulness, gentleness and self-control; and here there is no conflict with Jewish laws." (TLB; emphasis added)

10. Psalm 127:3 "**Children are a gift from God**; they are his reward." (TLB; emphasis added)

James 1:17 "**But whatever is good and perfect comes to us from God, the Creator of all light, and he shines forever without change or shadow.**" (TLB; emphasis added)

'I Spied' God...

On this day, I agreed that Jesus is God's Son and believed in my heart
that He made me clean when His Father raised Him from the dead. Then
I told someone special that I love and trust Jesus now. I know that I have His Holy Spirit in
me and He will help me with everything in my life. (Romans 10:9-10 & Ephesians 1:13-14)

Date: _____

Since then, 'I Spy' The Holy Spirit is making me brave to...

_____

_____

_____

Date:_____

_____

_____

_____

Date:_____

_____

_____

_____

Date:_____

_____

_____

_____

Date:_____

_____

_____

_____

Date:_____

_____

_____

_____

Date:_____

_____

_____

_____

Date:_____

_____

_____

_____

Date:_____